RYA Introduction to Radar

Written in consultation with
Tim Bartlett FRIN
Edited by: Jon Mendez
Robert Avis

Published by
The Royal Yachting Association
RYA House Ensign Way Hamble
Southampton SO31 4YA

Tel: 0845 345 0400
Fax: 0845 345 0329
Email: info@rya.org.uk
Web: www.rya.org.uk

Design by Avalon Design+Print

Printed through World Print

British Cataloguing in Publication Date:
A Catalogue record of this book is available from the British Library.
ISBN:

CONTENTS

BACKGROUND BRIEFING

Marine radar is an electronic device which measures the bearing and distance of solid objects and presents this information in the form of a plan view, showing the location of objects such as land, navigation marks, and other vessels.

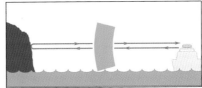

It works by transmitting short bursts of super high frequency radio energy (called microwaves) and receiving the echoes that are returned when these pulses of energy are reflected back from solid objects.

[handwritten: speed of light $c = 300 \times 10^6$ m/sec · 300/m sec]*

How radar measures distance (range)

Radio waves travel at an almost constant speed, so the time between a pulse being transmitted and its echo being received gives an indication of distance.

Radio waves travel at approximately 162,000 nautical miles per second, or 300 metres per microsecond. *[handwritten: microseconds]*

If a pulse is received 100 milliseconds after it was transmitted, it must have travelled 30,000 metres (30 kilometres).

This is the distance from the radar to the object and back, so the object must be 15 kilometres (about 8 nautical miles) away.

How radar measures direction (bearing)

Radar uses a continuously rotating aerial - often called a scanner - to measure the direction from which returning echoes are received.

The same aerial is used to transmit the microwave pulses, focussing them into a fairly narrow beam; rather as the reflector and lens of a lighthouse focus the light of its lamp.

The antenna rotates, usually at about 20rpm, to sweep the beam of microwave pulses around the horizon.

In principle, echoes will only be received from an object when the antenna is pointing at it - so if the radar knows which direction its scanner is pointing, it knows the direction of the object.

[handwritten: measures angle of target relative to ships bow direction]

Terminology

Pulse
refers to the short burst of microwave energy transmitted by the radar.

Echo
refers to the short burst of microwave energy returned to the radar from a target.

Target
refers to an object which returns an echo.

Contact
refers to the representation of a target on a radar screen - the blob.

Millisecond
one thousandth of a second.

Microsecond
one millionth of a second.

The parts of a radar set

All marine radars have five main parts, usually split between two main units: the **scanner unit** and the **display**, which are linked by a thick, multi-core cable. Which unit contains which parts varies between different makes and models: in older radars, especially, it is usual to find parts of the receiver in the scanner, and other parts in the display unit.

- Neither of the two units contains any user-serviceable parts or controls, and both may use potentially lethal voltages which may persist even after the radar has been switched off.

- Do NOT remove any part of the casing unless specifically told to do so by the manufacturer's instruction manual.

1. The main part of the **transmitter** is a special electronic valve called a magnetron, which produces short pulses of microwaves. In a typical small craft radar, each pulse lasts less than a microsecond, and they are repeated several hundred times a second.

2. The **TR Cell** (transmit receive cell) acts as a one-way valve: it allows pulses to travel from the transmitter to the antenna or from the antenna to the receiver, but does not allow the powerful pulses from the transmitter to reach the sensitive receiver.

3. The **antenna** focuses the microwaves into a fairly tight beam. It also catches the returning echoes, and passes them to the receiver.

4. The **receiver** receives the very weak echoes received, and amplifies them. Echoes from nearby objects are generally stronger than those from distant ones, so it amplifies the late-returning echoes more than those that arrive soon after the pulse was transmitted.

5. The **display** converts the range and bearing data from the scanner and receiver into a form that a human operator can understand — usually a plan view that is sometimes called a **Plan Position Indicator** or PPI.

6. The **trigger signal** tells the display when each pulse is transmitted, so that it can be compared with the amplified echoes arriving from the receiver.

7. The **heading mark signal** and **rotation signal** tell the display which way the antenna is pointing.

Frequency

All small craft radars transmit and receive at a frequency of about 9.4 Gigahertz (9400 million waves per second, or about 60 times higher than marine VHF radio), with a wavelength of just over 3 centimetres. For this reason, you may hear small craft radars described as **3-centimetre** or **X-band**, to distinguish them from the **10-centimetre** or **S-band** radars sometimes used by large ships.

The most important differences between small craft radars and those used by large ships is their size and power.

LIMITATIONS OF SMALL CRAFT RADAR

Power
Small craft radars typically transmit 1.5-5kW (1500-5000 Watts). This is about 1000 times more than a marine VHF, but it is small compared with the 25-50kW that is the norm for commercial ships.

The echoes, on which radar depends, are very much weaker than the original transmissions, so a low-powered radar is likely to miss objects which would be detected by a powerful one. This is applies particularly to small targets or poor reflectors: the effect on distant targets is very much less obvious.

Antenna size
The job of the antenna is to focus the outgoing transmissions into a narrow beam, and to measure the direction from which echoes return. A big antenna is very much better at both jobs than a small one, for instance:

Antenna width	Beam width
120cm	1.8°
60cm	3.9°
45cm	5.9°
30cm	8°

A narrow beam intensifies the radar transmissions, giving the effect of greater power. It also increases the precision with which the radar can measure the direction from which an echo is returning, and gives better discrimination (see page 13).

Display size
The display of a ship's radar gives a picture 180mm in diameter or more: for large ships, the minimum legal requirement is at least 340mm.

Small craft radars often have screens that are 7 inches across the diagonal, and give a picture about 100mm in diameter.

A small display is generally less clear than a larger one and:

- It is more difficult to spot small contacts, although this may be partly offset by a larger beam width, which makes all contacts look bigger.

- It is more difficult to distinguish the gaps between contacts that are close together.

Display resolution
Apart from a few very old radars, most displays use screens similar to those in TVs and PCs, in which the picture is made up of a mass of dots, called pixels.

A large, high-resolution screen may have ten times as many pixels as a small, low-resolution screen.

The high resolution screen will give a much more accurate indication of the shape of objects such as coastlines. The low resolution version will produce a more jagged image, and may make contacts look bigger than it should.

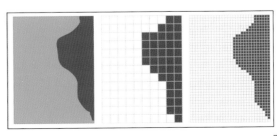

SWITCHING ON AND SETTING UP

There are many different makes and models of radar set, each with slightly different controls and operating procedures. Many of the more recent sets are highly automated, and will work well almost as soon as they are switched on. Some older sets, particularly those intended for commercial craft, may have a more complex set-up procedure.

Six controls are common to all marine radars, though in many modern sets they are buried in a menu system:

Controls

- Power on/off.
- Standby/Transmit.
- Brilliance.
- Gain.
- Range.
- Tuning.

Power on/off

Usually a push-button control, the power on/off control supplies power to the radar. When first switched on, a modern radar will carry out a short sequence of automated checks, before going through a warm-up phase. This is to protect the magnetron against the effects of sudden heating that would occur if it began transmitting while cold. The warm-up usually takes about two minutes, after which the set switches itself to standby.

Standby/Transmit

Often combined with the on/off switch, the standby/transmit control switches the radar between its standby mode — in which it is ready for use, with the transmitter warm but not operating — and the transmit mode, in which it is fully operational.

Brilliance and contrast

The brilliance control is exactly the same as the brightness control on a TV set: it adjusts the brightness of the picture to suit the ambient light and personal preference, but makes no difference to what is on the screen. It can be adjusted while the set is warming up or in standby mode.

Some radars with liquid crystal displays also have a contrast control. Like brilliance, it can be adjusted to suit the conditions and personal preference while the set is warming up or in standby mode. The optimum setting depends mainly on the direction from which you are viewing the screen.

Gain

Gain is the radar counterpart of the squelch control on a VHF radio: it regulates the sensitivity of the receiver. If it is set too high, the screen will be filled with a mass of speckles caused by radio 'noise'. If it is set too low, real echoes will be missed.

To adjust it, turn it up until the screen is filled with speckles, then turn it down until the speckles just disapear from most of the screen.

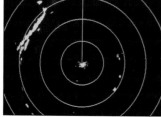
Gain too low

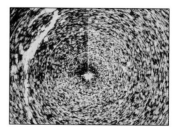
Gain too high

Range

should dedicate a battery to radar if use constantly b/c user leater that draws from batt.

The range control is used to adjust the area represented by the radar picture. If it is set to 12 miles, for instance, the outer ring of the picture represents a distance twelve miles from the centre.

Choosing a lower range reduces the area shown, but enlarges the image to show more detail, and vice versa.

Changing range also changes the duration of each pulse, and the interval between them.

Tuning

(typically auto tune)

Like any radio, a radar's receiver needs to be tuned to receive the particular frequency that is being transmitted. Although it is listening for echoes of its own transmissions, the frequency of those transmissions varies slightly, particularly as the magnetron warms up and cools down.

Adjust the tuning by selecting a long or medium range, and looking for a weak contact. Then adjust the tuning in small steps (either up or down). Allow about three seconds after each adjustment, for the picture to be refreshed using the new setting. Keep adjusting the tuning until the weak contact becomes as strong and bright as possible.

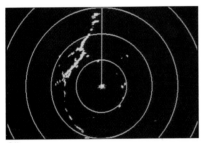

Off tune

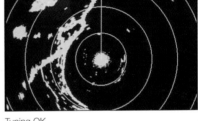

Tuning OK

Initial tuning may have such a marked effect that it may be necessary to re-adjust the gain, and continue tuning using a new weak target.

In any case, the tuning should be checked whenever the radar is switched on, and whenever there is a significant change in temperature and each time the radar range is changed. If there is no target in range, it is not possibble to tune the radar.

Set-up sequence

Of course the power has to be switched on first, and the radar switched to transmit, but the other controls are best adjusted in alphabetical order:

- *Brilliance (because you need to be able to see the picture before you can do anything else).*
- *Contrast (on LCDs only, but for the same reason).*
- *Gain (because tuning won't make any difference if the receiver is suppressing all echoes).*
- *Range (to ensure that there are some weak echoes within range).*
- *Tuning.*

Why bother?

Automatic set-up is good, and getting better, so why bother with manual controls?

It is rather like photography: a novice will probably find that an automatic camera will produce better results than if he fiddles with the controls of a sophisticated manual camera. A more skilful photographer, however, should get better results with a manual camera. In particularly difficult situations, the manual camera may produce dramatic pictures where the automatic camera will not work at all, the same is true of radar.

THE RADAR PICTURE

A typical radar picture consist of a pattern of concentric circles, with a straight line extending outwards from the centre. Your own vessel is at the centre of the pattern.

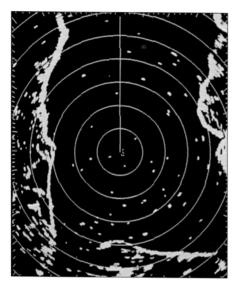

Range rings and heading mark

The circles are called **range rings**. They are equally spaced, to help judge distances on the radar picture: on the 12-mile range setting, for instance, range rings will be placed at 2, 4, 6, 8, 10, and 12 miles from the centre. If you do not want to use the range rings, or if you believe they may be hiding important information, there is always a facility for switching them off.

The straight line is called the **Heading Mark**. It stretches outward from the centre of the screen, to indicate the direction our vessel is pointing. If you believe the heading mark may be hiding important information, it can always be temporarily switched off, but it will come back on again as soon as the **Heading Mark Delete** control is released.

Heading modes

Head-Up

In the most basic radar installations, with no compass input, the heading mark points straight upwards. This is known as **Head-Up** mode.

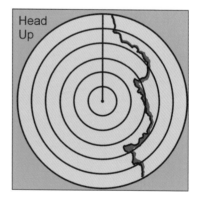

It has the advantage that targets on the port side of the boat show up as contacts on the left hand side of the screen, while those on the starboard side of the boat appear on the right hand side of the screen, and so on.

The disadvantage of head up mode is that as the boat yaws, the picture yaws with it, so objects which were directly ahead slide off to one side, while those which were on one side slide round towards the top or bottom of the picture.

North-Up

Most radars can accept heading information from an electronic compass, and can rotate the picture to put north at the top of the screen. This is known as **North-Up** mode.

This has the advantage that the radar picture is in the same orientation as the conventional navigational chart. It also stabilizes the picture: so long as the compass information is being

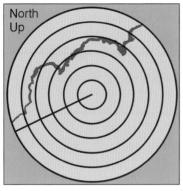

passed to the radar quickly enough, the picture appears to stand still: only the heading mark moves when the boat yaws.

The disadvantage is that many small boat navigators and skippers find it more difficult to interpret a collision situation in North-Up mode but this is through lack of practice rather than having a small craft radar set.

Course-Up

Course-Up mode is an attempt to combine the best of Head-Up and North-Up. It uses the same principle as North-Up, except that instead of north, the top of the screen represents whatever course the boat happened to be on at the moment Course-Up mode was selected. So long as you stay close to your original course, the heading mark remains almost upright, swaying from side to side as the boat yaws.

The advantage of Course-Up mode is that it is as easy to interpret as Head-Up, but without the problem of an unstable picture. The disadvantage is that if you forget to cancel the Course-Up mode after making a significant alteration of course, it can be highly disorientating, as the radar picture does not conform to the view from the cockpit or wheelhouse or to the chart.

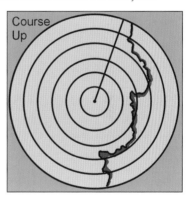

REFINING THE PICTURE

Despite appearances, the radar picture is not a map, nor is it a birds-eye-view: it is a diagrammatic representation of the echoes received from targets. Some things, particularly waves, rain and thunderclouds produce unwanted echoes that are quite capable of masking the echoes from real targets. These unwanted echoes are called **clutter**.

Sea clutter

Sea clutter is caused by radar pulses reflecting from the faces of nearby waves. More distant waves are less likely to create sea clutter, because their faces are obscured by other waves, while their crests scatter radio energy rather than to reflect it, so sea clutter appears as an irregular but fairly solid blob at the centre of the radar picture.

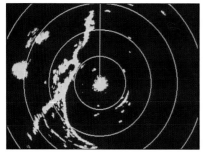
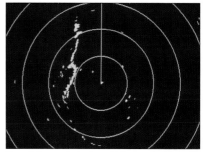

Sea clutter at centre of screen

Sea clutter control set too high

On motor boats, sea clutter is generally worst on the windward side, because the radar is looking at the steeper face of each wave. On sailing boats, the opposite is sometimes true, because when the boat heels over, the radar looks down to the water on the leeward side. In either case, sea clutter is worst in rough weather and for radars that are mounted high above the waterline.

Sea clutter can be reduced or removed by adjusting the sea clutter control - sometimes known as **anti-clutter (sea)** or **STC**. Used with care, this can hide the sea clutter, while allowing strong contacts that were hidden by the sea clutter to remain. It cannot, however, make contacts visible if their echoes are weaker than the sea clutter.

Used to excess, the sea clutter control can reduce the gain at the centre of the picture to such an extent that even strong echoes are suppressed, and substantial targets such as ships or land simply disappear.

Gain and sea clutter

The echoes on which radar depends are very weak indeed, particularly if they have come from a target at long range. A target at two miles, for instance, returns an echo sixteen times weaker than the same target at one mile. At four miles, it is 1/256 as strong as at one mile.

To overcome this, the returning echoes are subjected to several stages of amplification. One of these is controlled by the operator — the gain control. Another automatically increases the amplification applied to late-returning echoes, in order to counteract the weakening effect of distance.

The sea clutter control works by reducing the amplification applied to early-returning echoes.

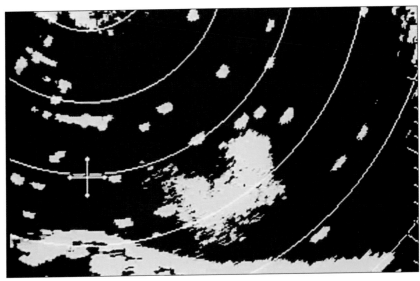
Rain clutter just below centre of picture

Rain clutter

Rain clutter looks similar to sea clutter: it is a mass of contacts forming a large, irregular blob. Unlike sea clutter, however, it may appear anywhere on the radar screen.

It is not necessarily caused by rain: large clouds (especially cumulonimbus) contain drops of water which may not reach the surface, but are still capable of producing the effect.

Rain clutter can be reduced or removed by adjusting the rain clutter control - sometimes known as **anti-clutter (rain) FTC**, or **differentiation**. On many small craft radars it is a simple on or off control but progressive controls, similar to those that operate gain and sea clutter, are becoming more common.

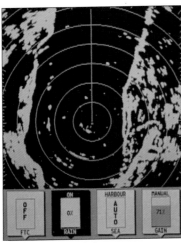
Coastlines on normal picture

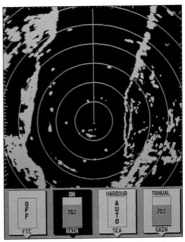
Coastlines with rain clutter control turned up: note how shelving coastline on right has been weakened

The rain clutter control can hide rain clutter, while generally having little effect on most ordinary contacts. It can, however weaken the echoes from gently shelving coastlines, and some progressive rain clutter controls can be turned up to such an extent that *all* contacts are suppressed.

More about rain clutter

An individual raindrop is far too small to produce a discernible echo. Many millions of them, however, can return sufficient energy to be detected by the radar's receiver, and produce a contact on the display. The echo produced by rain is quite different from that produced by a solid target such as a ship.

The ship produces a crisp, distinct echo, like a weakened version of the original pulse. Rain or cloud produces an even weaker echo that is more drawn out.

The rain clutter control works by cutting off all but the leading edge of each returning echo. This has little effect on crisp echoes, but significantly weakens those that are more drawn-out.

Interference

The atmosphere is full of radio **noise**, on many different frequencies, some of which can be detected by the radar's very sensitive receiver. This is what produces the background speckles that can be seen when the gain control is set too high. Careful tuning and gain adjustment will remove most of the interference, but strong interference on radar frequencies (such as is caused by other radars) is a more stubborn problem.

Interference from a single radar produces a distinctive pattern of spots laid out like the spokes of a wheel, but usually with a slight curve to each spoke. There are so many radars in use now that the distinctive pattern is seldom seen: radar interference appears just as apparently random spots.

Interference can be removed by switching the **interference rejection circuit** on.

It has no ill effects, so some recent radars do not have an operator control for it at all: it is permanently on. It should not, however, be used as a substitute for proper tuning and gain adjustment.

Echo stretch

Echo stretch is used to artificially enhance the radar picture by stretching each contact to make small contacts more conspicuous.

It is useful in situations such as when a lone watchkeeper is glancing occasionally at a radar screen, to back up a visual look-out for approaching ships.

Enlarging contacts, however, tends to hide details, so it is best to switch the echo stretch facility off when it is not required, and especially when using radar for accurate navigation or pilotage.

UNDERSTANDING THE PICTURE

Discrimination and beam width

No radar antenna is capable of transmitting a perfectly parallel-sided pencil beam, nor is it perfectly directional in receive mode.

The beam of a radar can be compared to the beam of a lighthouse or car headlamp: although most of the energy is concentrated within a narrow arc, the beam does not have perfectly-defined edges: some energy is transmitted outside the main beam.

In many cases this scattered energy forms separate beams that are weaker than the main beam but are still distinct: they are called **sidelobes**.

- The width of a radar beam means that even a very small target may produce quite a large contact, because it starts producing echoes as soon as one edge of the beam touches it, and goes on producing echoes until the beam has swept right over it.

- On a radar with a beam width of 6°, a small target such as a buoy is likely to appear as a contact about 6° across.

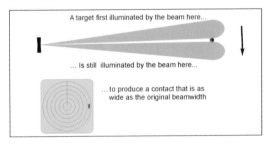

A target first illuminated by the beam here...

... is still illuminated by the beam here...

...to produce a contact that is as wide as the original beamwidth

- Gaps between objects such as buoys or headlands will appear correspondingly smaller: a harbour entrance, for instance, will not show up on radar until it is close enough for the radar beam to pass straight through without touching either side.

- On a radar with a 6° beam width, a harbour entrance 200 metres wide is unlikely to show up as a gap until it is less than a mile way.

- This is known as **bearing discrimination**

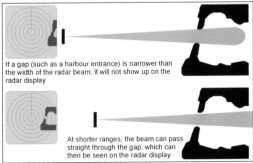

If a gap (such as a harbour entrance) is narrower than the width of the radar beam, it will not show up on the radar display

At shorter ranges, the beam can pass straight through the gap, which can then be seen on the radar display

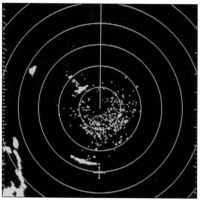

Vertical beam width

A radar beam is usually higher than it is wide. For small craft radars, the vertical beam width is usually about 25°-30°. This is to ensure that when the boat pitches or rolls, at least part of the beam will still be pointing towards the horizon.

The vertical beam width also explains why rain clouds produce strong echoes: at a range of six miles, a typical small boat radar will 'see' clouds up to an altitude of about 3,000 metres.

The ship passing astern (just below and left of centre) is producing side lobe echoes

- A good reflector at close range (such as a passing ship) will produce echoes that are strong enough to be received, even from the weak **sidelobes**, so it will show up as a string of targets, all at the same range but on different bearings so that they form a curve or circle around the centre of the picture.

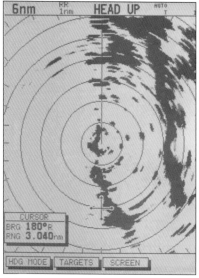

This picture is a radar screen resolved from a 6° beam width

DISCRIMINATION, PULSE LENGTH, AND PRF

Although the radar pulses are very short, each pulse lasts a measurable length of time. For a typical small craft radar, operating at a range of 6 miles, each pulse lasts about 1 microsecond. So by the time the trailing edge of the pulse emerges from the antenna, its leading edge has already travelled about 300 metres.

Now suppose the radar pulse comes across two targets on the same bearing, but one at slightly greater range than the other. If the difference in range is less than half the pulse length, the leading edge of the echo from the more distant target will catch up with the trailing edge of the echo from the nearer one.

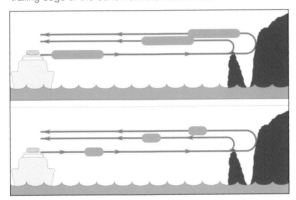

On the radar screen, the two targets would appear as one long one.

The problem can be solved by using a much shorter pulse length. A radar with a pulse length of 0.1 microsecond should be able to discriminate between two targets that are just 15 metres apart.

Such short pulses do not contain sufficient energy to produce receivable echoes at long range. Long pulses can travel much further, so it is important to make sure that the early echoes from one pulse do not get muddled up with late-returning echoes from the one before. This is achieved by allowing a much longer interval between pulses - typically a thousandth of a second or more.

If the gaps between pulses are increased, the number of pulses per second must decrease, so long pulses are always associated with a low **pulse repetition frequency (PRF)**.

- On most small craft radars, pulse length and PRF are changed automatically to suit the range scale in use.

What reflects?

Five factors determine whether a target is a good reflector or not. They are:

- Material.
- Size.
- Shape.
- Orientation.
- Texture.

Material

Strictly speaking, radar waves are not reflected at all: they are absorbed and re-radiated. The way in which they are affected by this process depends on the material.

- Anything which conducts electricity is likely to be a good reflector.
- Anything which does not conduct electricity is likely to be a poor reflector.

Size

A large object can absorb and re-radiate more energy than a small one.

Shape

Flat surfaces generally behave rather like mirrors, and radiate most of the reflected energy in one direction. Unfortunately, if the flat surface is not at exactly the right angle, it may reflect the energy in the wrong direction.

- Flat surfaces are generally strong but unreliable reflectors.

Curved surfaces tend to scatter the energy. Surfaces which curve in two directions (i.e. a sphere, as opposed to a cylinder) are worst in this respect. On the other hand, you can be certain that there will always be some small part of the surface of a spherical target that will be at the perfect angle to reflect energy back to the antenna.

- Curved surfaces are generally weak but consistent reflectors.

Orientation

A flat surface is a good reflector only when it is at exactly the right angle to the radar beam.

In practice, most real targets are made up of a combination of nearly flat and curved surfaces, but their ability to reflect radar pulses is still affected by their orientation. A ship that is broadside-on for instance, is likely to be a better reflector than one which is at an angle.

Texture

A rough surface ensures that at least part of the target is likely to be at a suitable angle to reflect radar energy back the way it came. It makes a weaker but much more reliable echo than a smooth surface.

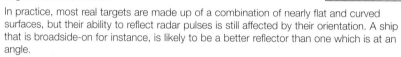

In this context rough means that it has surface irregularities that are comparable in size with the wavelength of radar (a few centimetres).

What shows up?

The table below involves some sweeping generalisations, but it shows that you can reasonably expect to see land and ships at quite long range. It also shows why the skippers of small craft should never assume that they are visible on another vessel's radar.

	Land	Ships	Boats	Buoys	Waves
Material	Good	Good	Poor	Good	Good
Size	Good	Good	Poor	Poor	Varies
Shape	Varies	Varies	Varies	Varies	Varies
Orientation	Varies	Varies	Varies	Varies	Varies
Texture	Good	Good	Poor	Good	Good
Overall	Good	Good	Poor	Moderate	Moderate

An empty plastic cup in a microwave cooker is unlikely to become hot because it does not absorb the microwaves: it is effectively transparent to microwaves. If you do the same thing with the cup full of water, the water absorbs the microwave energy and converts it to heat.

BLIND AREAS

A radar pulse can only produce an echo if it reaches a target.

There are several types of obstruction that can prevent it from doing so.

Obstructions on board

Obstructions on board the vessel, such as masts, funnels, superstructure, or cargo can obstruct the out-going pulse, and may even reflect it so that it is transmitted in some completely different direction.

An obstruction which is significantly narrower than the width of the radar antenna itself may cause a slight reduction in the effective transmitted power. An obstruction which is the same width as the antenna or wider may cause blind arcs, in which no target can be detected.

Shadow areas (1)

Radar cannot see round corners, so headlands and hills obscure features beyond them from radar, just as they obscure them from the naked eye.

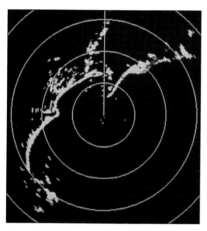 

Compare the radar picture with the map. On the radar picture, note the lack of detail where the coastline is hidden beyond a headland. Note also that the headland in the bottom left appears to be an island: the low ground to the north of it is below the radar horizon. A map (right) of the same area, shows the missing coastline

Shadow areas (2)

A completely different kind of shadow-area occurs all round any substantial contact. It is caused by the combined effect of beam width, pulse length, and pixel size, and refers to the fact that when two targets are close together, the contacts that represent them will merge together, to form a single contact - as though the small contact had disappeared into a pool of shadow around the larger one.

Radar horizon

Radar waves travel in almost straight lines, so distant objects may be hidden below the horizon, just as they are hidden from normal sight.

Radar waves bend very slightly as they pass through the atmosphere, so they follow the

...urvature of the Earth slightly better than light waves. This makes the radar horizon about ...0% more distant than the visual horizon.

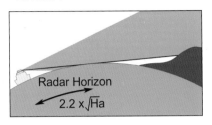

The formula for calculating the distance to the radar horizon is:

Distance = 2.2 x √height of the antenna

where the distance is in nautical miles and the height of the antenna is in metres.

For a radar antenna 4 metres above sea level:

Distance = $2.2 \times \sqrt{4}$

Distance = 2.2×2

Distance = 4.4 miles

An object may become visible to radar when its radar horizon meets or overlaps the observer's radar horizon.

A 100 metre cliff has a radar horizon of:

Distance = $2.2 \times \sqrt{100}$

Distance = 2.2×10

Distance = 22 miles

So it may appear on a radar whose antenna is 4 metres above the waterline when the range is:

22 + 4.4 = 26.4 miles or less

This means that:

- Low-lying coastlines cannot be expected to appear at long range.
- Hills or mountains inland may appear on radar before the coastline.
- High headlands may appear to be islands.

Super refraction and sub refraction

Occasionally, weather conditions may make the radar beam bend more or less than usual, increasing or decreasing the distance to the horizon.

Sub refraction occurs when the air temperature is cooler than the sea, and tends to reduce the distance to the radar horizon.

Super refraction is generally associated with fine settled weather and high pressure systems, in which humid air is trapped close to the sea surface: it bends the radar beam more than usual, and increases the distance to the radar horizon.

Extra super-refraction is a particularly extreme form of super-refraction, sometimes known as ducting, in which the radar beam is trapped close to the Earth's surface, almost eliminating the effect of the horizon.

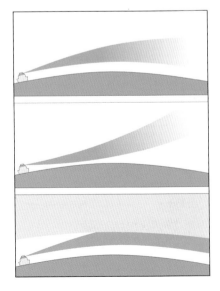

RADAR REFLECTORS

Targets such as small craft, buoys, piles and beacons do not produce strong echoes. To make them more conspicuous on radar, they are often fitted with radar reflectors.

Radar reflectors may be divided into two main groups:

Passive reflectors.

Active reflectors (or transponders).

Radar cross section (RCS)

To compare the performance of different reflectors, we need a consistent standard of measurement. This is achieved by comparing the echo received from the reflector with the echo that would be received from a spherical metal target at the same range.

An object described as having a **radar cross section** or **equivalent echoing area** of 10 square metres produces the same strength of echo as a metal sphere with a cross sectional area of 10 square metres (a diameter of 3.6 metres).

Note that a sphere is chosen because of its consistent performance, not because of its efficiency.

* A flat metal plate, the size of this book (A5) would have a radar cross section of 10.6 square metres, if it were at right angles to the radar beam.

The radar cross section of most targets varies considerably, depending on the direction from which they are struck by the radar pulses. The changing RCS is often represented graphically by polar diagrams or target pattern maps.

Passive reflectors

Passive reflectors rely on their shape and construction to achieve a compromise between the reflective efficiency of a flat metal plate and the consistent performance of a metal sphere.

There are two main types:

Corner reflectors (eg Echomax, Firdell)

Corner reflectors use flat metal plates (usually of aluminium) arranged at right angles to each other.

Three square plates can be arranged to form an **octahedral** shape. If it is placed on a horizontal surface, it will have six internal corners pointing almost horizontally, but 60 degrees apart. Radar energy entering an internal corner is reflected straight back the way it entered.

Stacked arrays use the same principle, but are constructed to offer more corners. There are numerous designs, usually enclosed in plastic housings for protection.

Lens reflectors (eg Cyclops, Visiball)

Lens reflectors use the same principle as cats eyes on the road: internal reflections within a ball (or a series of concentric shells) of a special plastic directs the beam of radar energy back the way it came.

Unfortunately:

* Very few passive reflectors produce a perfectly consistent response.
* Even at a range of just six miles, the size of a typical passive reflector is such that it catches less than 0.00005% of the energy transmitted by a typical ship's radar.
* Carrying a passive radar reflector does not guarantee that you will be visible.

Active reflectors

Active reflectors are sometimes called transponders, because they contain receivers and transmitters operating on microwave frequencies. When a radar pulse is received, a transponder transmits its own pulse in reply. There are three distinct types:

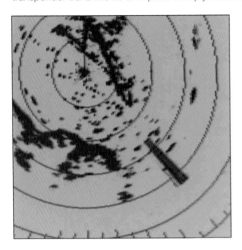

Racons

Racons are fitted to some buoys and navigation marks, to make them more conspicuous.

A racon scans slowly up and down the radar frequencies. When it receives a radar pulse, it responds by transmitting a much longer pulse on the same frequency. This reply pulse may be broken up to form a character in the Morse Code.

On the radar screen, a racon response looks like a very long echo, extending from the target out towards the edge of the screen. As the racon sweeps through the frequency range, **racon flash** on the screen alternately fades and intensifies.

Radar Target Enhancers (RTEs)

A radar target enhancer is a device carried on board which scans all the X-band radar frequencies simultaneously. When it receives a pulse, it responds by immediately transmitting a replica pulse, similar to the echo that would be produced by a passive reflector, but stronger. This makes your vessel appear larger than it actually is. Radar target enhancers need to be used with care in busy areas as they may lead another vessel to think that your vessel is much larger than it is.

Search and Rescue Transponders (SARTs)

A SART is a portable piece of equipment providing a means of sending a distress alert to another vessel with radar. Instead of responding with a single pulse, like an RTE, a SART responds with a string of twelve pulses, with a short pause between each one. The radar cannot tell that these are all from the same object: it displays them as a line of twelve echoes, all on the same bearing, but 0.6 mile apart.

As the name suggests, SARTs are intended primarily for use in liferafts, to reduce the search effort required.

* A SART must not be activated except in a distress situation.

FIXING POSITION BY RADAR

The three-point fix

A traditional navigation technique known as a three point fix involves measuring the bearing (direction) of each of three landmarks.

The line of sight between the boat and each landmark can be represented as a pencil line on the chart, by drawing a line along the measured bearing, passing through the landmark concerned. The boat's position must then lie somewhere on that line.

The only place the boat can be on two such lines simultaneously is the point at which they cross.

When three lines are involved, they should all cross at a single point, but in practice they never do: instead, they form a triangle known as a **cocked hat**. It is not necessarily true to say that your position is somewhere inside the cocked hat. Nevertheless, the size of the cocked hat is a useful indicator of the reliability of the fix, because each line acts as a cross-check on the other two.

The cocked hat can be kept small by:

- Positively identifying the landmarks on the chart as well as in the real word.
- Taking bearings as accurately as possible.
- Taking bearings as quickly as possible.
- Choosing objects that are well spread around the horizon.
- Choosing near objects rather than distant ones.
- Taking bearings that are changing quickly, last.

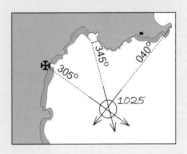

The three-point fix by radar bearings

All practical marine radars are equipped with an **Electronic Bearing Line (EBL)**. It is a straight line, radiating outwards from the centre to the edge of the screen, which can be swept round the screen like the second-hand of a watch.

- The bearing represented by the EBL is usually displayed in a data box somewhere on the screen.
- If the radar is not interfaced to a compass, the bearing shown will be relative, i.e. it will be a number of degrees, measured clockwise from the heading mark.
- If the radar is interfaced to a compass, the bearing may have been converted to compass, magnetic, or true.

It is possible to take a three point fix by using the EBL instead of a hand bearing compass, so long as you remember:

- Objects such as churches and lighthouses do not usually show up on radar.
- The bearing of the edge of a piece of land needs to be adjusted to allow for the beam width, by placing the EBL so that it cuts through the tip of the headland, rather than brushing it. Allow half the beam width.
- On a Head-Up radar, you will have to correct each bearing for the course being steered.

Radar is generally not good at measuring bearings. Other errors such as helmsman error or arithmetical mistakes make it even worse. **Fixing by radar bearings is possible, but not recommended.**

To convert from relative to true

A relative bearing can be converted to a true bearing by adding your heading to the bearing. If the answer is more than 360°, subtract 360° from it.

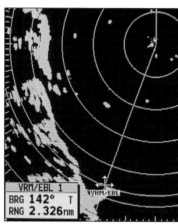

VRM/EBL 1
BRG 142° T
RNG 2.326nm

eg	Bearing	265°	Relative
	Heading	317°	Compass
		582°	
	Subtract	360°	
		222°	Compass
	Deviation	002°E	Add East, Subtract West
		224°	Magnetic
	Variation	004°W	Add East, Subtract West
		220°	

The three-point fix by radar ranges

All modern marine radars are equipped with a **Variable Range Marker (VRM)**. It is an adjustable range ring, whose radius can be varied by the operator, and used to measure the distance to chosen targets. The actual radius of the VRM at any moment is displayed in a data box adjacent to the radar screen.

The principle of a fix by ranges is that if a landmark is two miles away from you, you must also be two miles away from the landmark. In other words, you are somewhere on a circle, with a radius of two miles, and its centre at the landmark. The circle can be represented on a chart by using a drawing compass or a pair of dividers to scribe a circle on the chart, with a radius corresponding to the measured range.

Repeating the process three times, using different well-spread landmarks, produces three intersecting position lines. Where they cross represents the boat's position.

Radar ranges are generally accurate, and are not afflicted by arithmetical error or helmsman error.

The same six rules apply as to traditional three-point fixes:

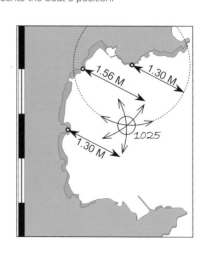

- Identify the landmarks on the chart as well as on the radar screen.

- Measure ranges as accurately as possible (use the shortest practical range scale).

- Measure ranges as quickly as possible.

- Choosing landmarks that are well spread around the horizon.

- Choosing near objects rather than distant ones (and use the shortest practical range scale).

- Measure ranges that are changing quickly (i.e. those ahead or astern), last.

PILOTAGE BY RADAR

Radar can be a very powerful pilotage tool, particularly in poor visibility or darkness, but using it effectively takes practice, so it is a good idea to refer to it frequently, even in good conditions.

Eyeball pilotage

The simplest kind of radar pilotage is similar to eyeball pilotage.

Just as a well-defined channel can sometimes be followed simply by aiming for the middle, it can also be followed by radar, by steering the boat so as to keep the heading mark pointing towards the most open water.

Similarly, the edge of a buoyed channel can sometimes be followed by aiming for one buoy after another.

The radar versions of eyeballing and buoy-hopping suffer the same problems as their naked-eye counterparts:

- Keep track of where you are and where you should be going next: take care not to miss a buoy, or follow the wrong channel.
- Be aware of any hazards that will not show up on radar (such as shallow water).
- Be careful that you are not being swept off track by a strong wind or tidal stream.

Clearing ranges

Clearing bearings are often used in traditional pilotage. Their radar counterparts are clearing ranges.

Suppose, for instance, that there is a dangerous underwater rock half a mile off the coast. So long as you are more than 0.6 mile off the coast, you cannot hit the rock. So if you set the VRM to 0.6 mile, and make sure that the coastline never appears inside the VRM, you will stay clear of the hazard.

Alternatively, you may choose to go inside the rock. In this case, you know you will clear the rock so long as you stay within 0.4 miles of the coast. To do this, you would set the VRM to 0.4 miles, and make sure that some part of the coastline was always inside the VRM.

Clearing ranges - practical example

The illustration shows the approaches to a harbour, with the deep-water channel running north-westwards along the eastern shore. From the south-west, the approach is partly blocked by a long sand-bank, but there is a useful short-cut through the middle of the sand bank.

The short cut lies parallel to the western shore: the first stage of the approach involves keeping between 0.65M and 0.75M from the wall. 0.25M from the eastern shore, it is time to turn hard to port, towards the harbour entrance, taking care to stay at least 0.1M from the eastern shore.

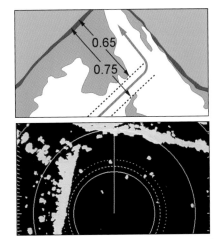

Parallel indexing

Parallel indexing is based on the principle that if you know the track you are intending to follow, it is possible to predict the way a fixed landmark - known as the reference target - will appear to move on the radar screen.

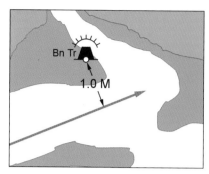

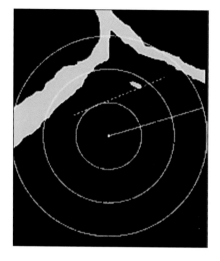

If our intended track is from west to east, passing a mile south of a buoy, we should see the buoy on radar, a mile to the north of us, and apparently moving for east to west. Some radar sets include facilities for drawing lines electronically on their screens: alternatively, it is possible to use a grease pencil or whiteboard marker to draw either on the glass of the screen itself or on a protective acetate sheet placed in front of it

If the contact representing the buoy does, indeed, behave exactly as predicted, we must be following the intended track.

If it does not - if it slips closer to the centre than it is supposed to, for instance, then clearly something is going wrong and we need to take steps to correct it by altering course away from the buoy in order to get it back onto its planned line.

The conventional way to draw a parallel index line on a radar screen is to set the VRM to the **cross index range** (i.e. the shortest distance between the reference target and the intended track), and to draw a line, touching the VRM, parallel to the intended track.

An alternative is to think in terms of waypoints - by asking yourself "what will be the range and bearing of the reference target from each waypoint in turn?". When the results are plotted onto the radar screen, the resulting line should look very much like the intended track on the chart, scaled to suit the radar and rotated through 180°.

* **Parallel indexing is only effective on North-Up radars.**

COLLISION AVOIDANCE

Relative motion

Your own vessel is always at the centre of the radar picture. If you are moving towards a stationary object, such as a buoy, the radar picture will give the impression that you are stationary and that the buoy is moving towards you. This is known as relative motion: the radar shows the buoy's changing position relative to your own vessel, rather than its fixed position on the surface of the Earth.

If you are dealing with a moving object, then its relative motion depends on its own movement as well as on yours.

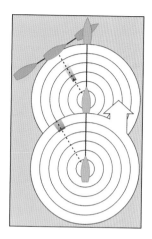

* The movement of the **contact** across the **radar screen** is seldom an accurate representation of the **target's** movement across the **Earth**.

What the IRPCS rules say

Rule 5

Rule 5 of the International Regulations for the Prevention of Collisions at Sea says:

"Every vessel shall at all times maintain a proper lookout by sight and hearing as well as by all available means appropriate in the prevailing circumstances and conditions so as to make a full appraisal of the situation and of the risk of collision."

Rule 6

Rule 6 says:

"Every vessel shall at all times proceed at a safe speed."

Among the factors listed in determining a safe speed it includes:

The characteristics of the radar equipment.

The effect of the sea state and weather on radar detection.

The possibility that small vessels may not be detected.

The number of vessels detected by radar.

Rule 7

Rule 7 says:

"Every vessel shall use all available means appropriate to the prevailing circumstances and conditions to determine if the risk of collision exists."

"Proper use shall be made of radar equipment if fitted and operational, including long-range scanning and radar plotting."

"Such risk (of collision) shall be deemed to exist if the compass bearing of an approaching vessel does not appreciably change."

Rule 7 is one of the Rules which apply in any state of visibility. However as skipper of your vessel you decide what is most "appropriate to the prevailing circumstances and conditions", for example a yacht skipper may be conserving battery power in good visibility.

Rule 19

Rule 19 is a long and complicated rule which applies to vessels which are not in sight of one another. In other words, if you detect another vessel by radar alone, your avoiding action must be based on Rule 19, rather than on the normal rules.

Key features of rule 19 are:

- There is no **give-way** or **stand-on** vessel.
- Avoid altering course to port for vessels forward of the beam unless overtaking.
- Avoid altering course towards vessels abeam or abaft the beam.

Assessing risk

This **steady-bearing** test referred to in Rule 7 can be carried out by using the EBL as the radar equivalent of a hand bearing compass.

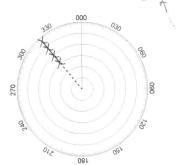

If the contact representing the other vessel appears to slide straight along the EBL, the implication is that it is on a steady bearing, and that there is therefore a risk of collision.

Unless someone does something to change the situation, the contact will continue to slide along the EBL until it reaches the centre of the screen - the position already occupied by your own boat.

How near is a near miss?

Even if the EBL test suggests that there is not likely to be a collision, it is useful to know how near any near miss is likely to be, using a process known as **plotting**.

- The range and bearing of the contact in question can be measured (using the EBL and VRM), and transferred onto a paper **plotting sheet**.
- Alternatively, use a grease pencil or dry-wipe marker to plot directly on the glass screen of the radar itself, or onto an acetate or acrylic sheet laid over it.

If neither you nor the other vessel alters course or speed, the plot should show the contact moving at a steady speed and in a straight line. Unless one or the other of you does something to change the situation, it will continue moving at the same speed and in the same direction, so after the first few plots it is possible to predict the contact's future movement, and from this judge how close it will get to the centre of the screen.

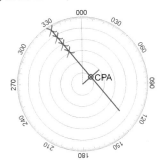

This distance, between the centre of the screen and the line representing the predicted movement of the contact, represents the **Closest Point of Approach - CPA**, or the nearest part of the near miss.

- If the line showing the projected movement of the contact cuts through our heading mark, the target will cross ahead of us.
- If it crosses below the centre of the screen, we are about to pass in front of the target.

What is he doing?

A contact that is on a steady bearing cannot be heading straight for you unless it is dead ahead or dead astern or you are stopped. It is really heading for the point somewhere in front of you, where the collision will happen unless one of you does something about it.

To decide what to do about it, it is useful to know the other vessel's course and speed.

To do this, we must remove the effect of our own movement, by showing the other vessel's movement relative to a stationary object. This need not be a real stationary object: it can be an imaginary object, drawn onto the radar screen.

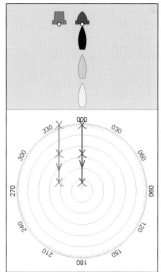

The contact representing an object that is stationary (but drifting with the tide) will always:

- Move parallel to the heading marker.
- Move in the opposite direction to the heading marker.
- Move at the same speed as our own speed through the water.

When you first see a contact that you think may represent a collision threat, start plotting its position, either on screen or on a plotting sheet. Label its position with the time.

From that first position, draw a line parallel to the heading marker, but in the opposite direction, to represent the movement of the imaginary buoy.

Measuring along that line, mark off distances corresponding to the distance you will have travelled in whatever time interval you have chosen. In 6 minutes at 5 knots, for instance, you will have travelled 0.5 mile, or in 3 minutes (a twentieth of an hour) at 20 knots, you will have travelled 1.0 mile.

After that time interval, mark the new position of the contact.

The line between the contact's new position and the position of the imaginary buoy represents the direction and distance the other vessel has travelled in the time interval you chose.

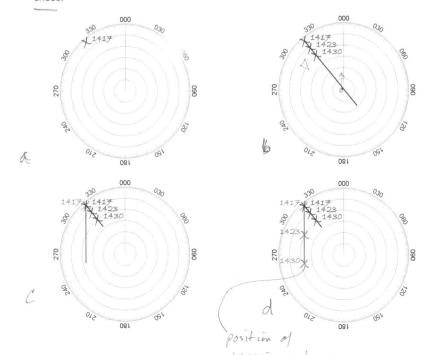

position of imaginary buoy

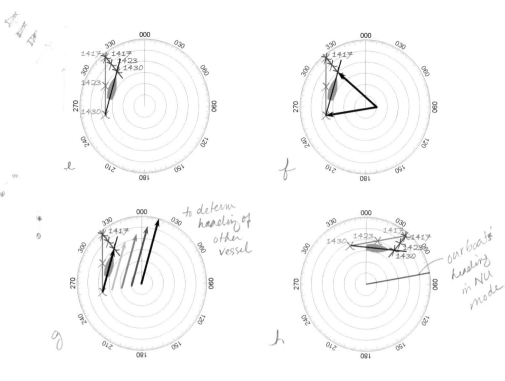

Some people like to label the corners of the triangle with the letters O, W, and A.

- O represents the **O**riginal position of the contact.
- WO represents the **W**ay of your **O**wn vessel.
- OA represents the **O**bserved or **A**pparent movement of the contact.
- WA represents the **W**ay of **A**nother vessel.

Guard zones

Most small craft radars include a facility known as a **guard zone**. This allows the operator to electronically mark certain areas of the screen: the radar will then sound an alarm whenever a contact appears in the marked area. It is useful as an 'extra pair of eyes' for short-handed sailors, but cannot be relied upon: the alarm may be triggered by land, by large waves, or by vessels which pose no threat, while potential collision threats may pass outside the guard zone or not appear on screen until they have passed through it.

ARPA

Radars installed on many commercial vessels include an accessory known as ARPA (Automatic Radar Plotting Aid), which can automatically calculate the courses, speeds, and CPA's (Closest Point of Approach) of approaching contacts.

Cut down versions, which may not meet the stringent requirements of the IMO (International Maritime Organisation), known as MARPA (Mini ARPA) or ATA (Automatic Tracking Aids), are built into some small craft radars.

Details vary between different makes and models, but in most cases, the operator uses the radar's cursor to select contacts which are of interest. The MARPA/ATA marks each contact, usually with a square box. After about a minute, when it has gathered enough information, it changes the symbol (usually to a circle), with a line indicating the direction and speed at which the contact is moving across the screen. At the same time, information such as the target's course, speed, CPA, and time to CPA are displayed in a data box on the screen.

The operator can also set up various criteria (such as CPA or time to CPA) which he considers 'dangerous'. The equipment will then sound an alarm if it detects a dangerous contact, and changes its symbol to a triangle.

To achieve all this, the tracking aid needs information about your own vessel's course and speed, from other instruments. If the information is provided by your vessel's Log and Compass, it is known as **sea stabilised**, because it shows courses and speeds relative to the water. If, instead, it takes track and velocity from a GPS receiver, it is known as **ground stabilised**, because it shows courses and speeds relative to the sea bed.

In a three-knot tidal stream, for instance:

- A sea stabilised ARPA would show a drifting yacht as stationary, but would show a moored buoy as moving up-tide at three knots.

- A ground stabilised ARPA would show the drifting yacht as moving down-tide at three knots, but would show the moored buoy as stationary.

Automatic tracking aids carry out their calculations far more quickly, and update them more frequently than any human operator. Of course this is useful, but it means that small errors in the data supplied to the equipment can cause significant errors in the information it gives back. In particular, small craft tracking aids are prone to:

- Bearing error caused by beamwidth distortion.

- Heading error caused by a poorly calibrated heading sensor.

- Heading error caused by a slow data link between the compass and radar.

- Speed error caused by a poorly calibrated log or rapidly fluctuating boat speed.

- Target swap when two targets pass so close to each other that they form a single contact before separating again: the equipment may lose track of which is which.

ARPA, ATA, or MARPA can be a valuable aid, particularly in congested waters and in conjunction with a large, well set-up radar and instruments, but it is important to treat its information with caution, especially when the CPA is small.

GLOSSARY

A/C (rain)	anti-clutter rain: another name for the rain clutter control.
A/C (sea)	anti-clutter sea: another name for the sea clutter control.
ARPA	Automatic Radar Plotting Aid: a device to calculate the course, speed, and CPA and other useful information about targets on screen.
ATA	Automatic Tracking Aid: an alternative term for MARPA.
contact	the representation of a target on a radar screen — the blob.
course	the direction in which a vessel is supposed to be pointing: ideally, the same as the average heading over a period of time.
CPA	Closest Point of Approach.
CRT	Cathode Ray Tube: a type of graphic display typically used for television sets and desk-top computers.
differentiation	an alternative term for rain clutter control.
EBL	Electronic Bearing Line: a line on the radar display used to measure the bearing of a target.
echo	the short burst of microwave energy returned to the radar from a target
EEA	Equivalent Echoing Area: an alternative term for RCS.
expansion	an alternative term for echo stretch.
FTC	Fast Time Constant: an alternative term for rain clutter control.
GHz	GigaHertz.
gigaHertz	a unit of frequency equal to 1,000,000,000 Hertz. 1 Hertz is one cycle per second.
heading	the direction a vessel is pointing at any given moment.
kW	kilowatt: a unit of power equal to 1000 Watts.
LCD	Liquid Crystal Display: a type of graphic display characterised by compact size and low power consumption.
magnetron	the component which generates microwave pulses.
MARPA	Mini Automatic Radar Plotting a simplified version of ARPA fitted to some small craft radars.
microsecond	one millionth of a second.
millisecond	one thousandth of a second.
ms	millisecond.

PI	Parallel Index: a pilotage technique, or a marking on the screen intended to assist with pilotage.
PPI	Plan Position Indicator: the radar display.
PRF	Pulse Repetition Frequency: the number of pulses transmitted per second.
PRI	Pulse Repetition Interval the time interval from the start of one pulse to the start of the next.
pulse	a short burst of microwave energy transmitted by a radar.
racon	a device which transmits a distinctive pulse in response to a radar pulse received.
RCS	Radar Cross Section: the ability of a target to reflect radar energy, compared with a sphere of 1 square metre cross section.
RPM	revolutions per minute.
RTE	Radar Target Enhancer: a device which transmits a pulse in response to a radar pulse received.
SART	Search and Rescue Transponder: a device which transmits a distinctive pattern of pulses in response to a radar pulse received, used by vessels in distress and liferafts.
S-band	radars with an operating frequency of about 3GHz.
scanner	a radar's antenna: the component that radiates the microwave energy.
STC	Sensitivity Time Control: an alternative term for sea clutter control.
swept gain	an alternative term for sea clutter control.
target	an object which returns an echo.
TR cell	a switch which changes the radar set from transmit to receive.
track	the direction in which a vessel is actually moving: may be referred to the ground (ground track) or to the water (water track).
VRM	Variable Range Marker: a circle on the radar display used to measure the bearing of a target.
X-band	radars with an operating frequency of about 9.4GHz.
ms	microsecond.

Text paper

Elemental
Chlorine Free

Sustainable
Forests

EMAS
VERIFIED
ENVIRONMENTAL
MANAGEMENT

Cover paper

Totally Chlorine
Free

Sustainable
Forests

EMAS
VERIFIED
ENVIRONMENTAL
MANAGEMENT

RYA *Membership*

Promoting and Protecting Boating
www.rya.org.uk

RYA Membership

Promoting and Protecting Boating

The RYA is the national organisation which represents the interests of everyone who goes boating for pleasure.

The greater the membership, the louder our voice when it comes to protecting members' interests.

Apply for membership today, and support the RYA, to help the RYA support you.

Benefits of Membership

- Access to expert advice on all aspects of boating from legal wrangles to training matters
- Special members' discounts on a range of products and services including boat insurance, books, videos and class certificates
- Free issue of certificates of competence, increasingly asked for by everyone from overseas governments to holiday companies, insurance underwriters to boat hirers

- Access to the wide range of RYA publications, including the quarterly magazine
- Third Party insurance for windsurfing members
- Free Internet access with RYA-Online
- Special discounts on AA membership
- Regular offers in RYA Magazine
- ...and much more

Join now - membership form opposite

Join online at *www.rya.org.uk*

Visit our website for information, advice, members' services and web shop.

1 Important
To help us comply with Data Protection legislation, please tick *either* Box A or Box B (you must tick Box A to ensure you receive the full benefits of RYA membership). The RYA will not pass your data to third parties.

- [ ] **A.** I wish to join the RYA and receive future information on member services, benefits (as listed in RYA Magazine and website) and offers.
- [ ] **B.** I wish to join the RYA but do not wish to receive future information on member services, benefits (as listed in RYA Magazine and website) and offers.

When completed, please send this form to: **RYA, RYA House, Ensign Way, Hamble, Southampton, SO31 4YA**

2

Title	Forename	Surname	Date of Birth				Male	Female
			D D / M M / Y Y				[ ]	[ ]
1.								
2.			D D / M M / Y Y				[ ]	[ ]
3.			D D / M M / Y Y				[ ]	[ ]
4.			D D / M M / Y Y				[ ]	[ ]

Address

Town

County

Post Code

Evening Telephone

Daytime Telephone

email

Signature: _____ **Date:** _____

3 Type of membership required: *(Tick Box)*

- [ ] **Personal** *Before 1 October 2005 annual rate £33 or £30 by Direct Debit*
  From 1 October 2005 annual rate £37 or £34 by Direct Debit
- [ ] **Under 21** *Before 1 October 2005 annual rate £11 (no reduction for Direct Debit)*
  From October 2005 annual rate £12 (no reduction for Direct Debit)
- [ ] **Family*** *Before 1 October 2005 annual rate £50 or £47 by Direct Debit*
  From 1 October 2005 annual rate £56 or £52 by Direct Debit

* Family Membership: 2 adults plus any under 21s all living at the same address

4 Please tick ONE box to show your main boating interest.

- [ ] Yacht Racing
- [ ] Dinghy Racing
- [ ] Personal Watercraft
- [ ] Powerboat Racing
- [ ] Motor Boating
- [ ] Yacht Cruising
- [ ] Dinghy Cruising
- [ ] Inland Waterways
- [ ] Windsurfing
- [ ] Sportsboats and RIBs

Please see Direct Debit form overleaf

Instructions to your Bank or Building Society to pay by Direct Debit

Please complete this form and return it to:
Royal Yachting Association, RYA House, Ensign Way, Hamble, Southampton, Hampshire SO31 4YA

Originators Identification Number

9	5	5	2	1	3

To The Manager: Bank/Building Society

Address:

Post Code:

2. Name(s) of account holder(s)

3. Branch Sort Code

4. Bank or Building Society account number

Banks and Building Societies may not accept Direct Debit instructions for some types of account

5. RYA Membership Number (For office only)

6. Instruction to pay your Bank or Building Society

Please pay Royal Yachting Association Direct Debits from the account detailed in this instruction subject to the safeguards assured by The Direct Debit Guarantee.
I understand that this instruction may remain with the Royal Yachting Association and, if so, details will be passed electronically to my Bank/Building Society.

Signature(s)

Date

Office use / Centre Stamp

Cash, Cheque, Postal Order enclosed £
Made payable to the Royal Yachting Association

Office use only: Membership Number Allocated

077